ISLAM & ME
THE BABY GARDEN

by
ADEEBA JAFRI

Goodword**kidz**

Helping you build a family of faith

Tariq was an only child who lived with his mother and father.
One day, Tariq's mother told him "We're having a baby!"

Tariq was very happy that he was having a baby brother or sister but he also wondered where the baby would come from.

Tariq asked his friend Ali. "Ali, do you know where babies come from?" Ali replied, "Sure. There's a huge store that's filled with babies and one day, the mommy and daddy go to the store and pick one out. That's where babies come from."

Tariq thought a huge store filled with little babies was a very silly idea.

6

Tariq went to his friend Hasan and asked him, "Hasan, do you know where babies come from?" Hasan told his friend, "Of course! Babies come from a huge garden. You plant a baby seed in the ground, water it, and when the baby is ready, you pick it up and take it home. That's where babies come from." Have you ever heard of a baby garden? No, Tariq thought, that's too silly.

Tariq asked his friend Abdullah, "Abdullah, do you know where babies come from?" Abdullah had an even sillier answer. "Babies come in boxes!" Abdullah said. "You order the baby through the computer and it comes in the mail. That's where babies come from."

Lots of things come in the mail, but Tariq knew
that babies couldn't be one of them.

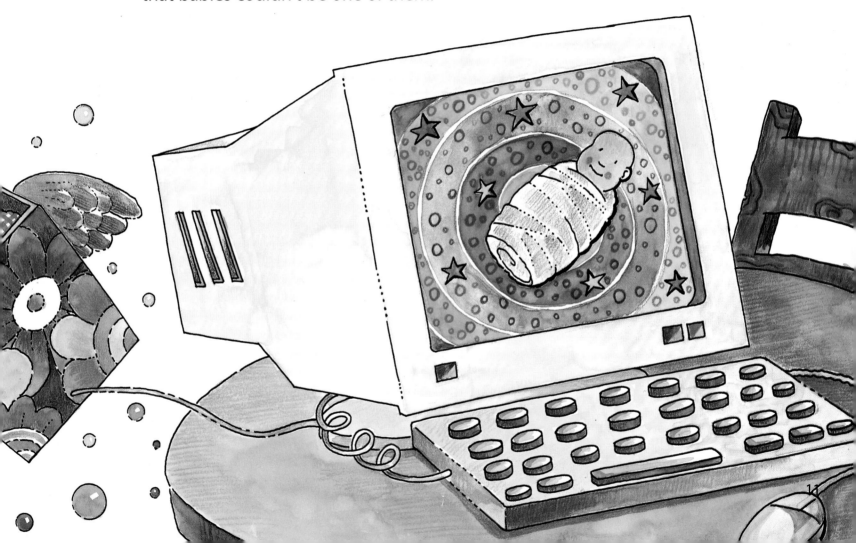

Poor Tariq. He was so confused. He had asked one friend after another and he still didn't know where babies came from.

Finally, Tariq asked his mother. "Ammi, where do babies come from?" Tariq's mother smiled and said, "Babies come from Allah. We make du'a to Allah (swt) to give us children and He is the only one that can grant this wish."

Tariq smiled. He felt so relieved!
This was the best answer of all.

Allah is the Creator of our universe and everything in it.

Can you find some of Allah's creations when you look in the sky?

What creations of Allah (swt) do you see… at the zoo? at the park? in your backyard?

There are some things in this world that Allah (swt) has given us the tools and the wisdom to make ourselves.

A house is made of wood, which comes from the trees that Allah created. A pizza is made from tomato sauce, which comes from the tomato plants that Allah created. It also comes from bread flour, made from wheat that grows in fields.

The Colors of Fruits

Red is an apple, shiny and sweet
Found high in the tree, delicious to eat

Orange is an orange that's round, whose skin
We peel to find the fruit within

Yellow is a banana, shaped like a moon
That grows in bunches and has many uses too.

Green is a pear that looks like a top
Wide at the bottom, short at the top.

Blue are blueberries, so small and yet sweet
Full of flavor they make a wonderful treat

These are the colors of fruits Allah (swt) made
Will you have some to eat today?

21

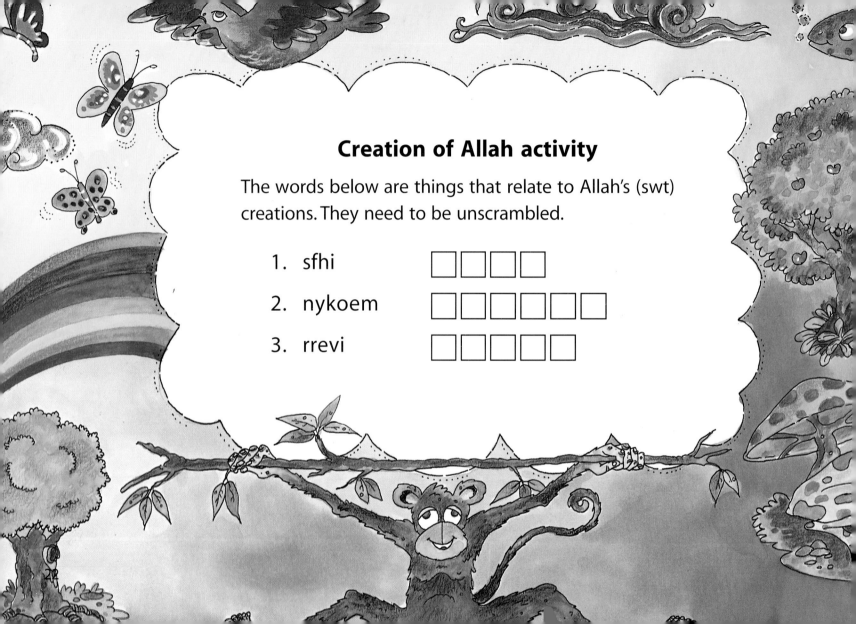

Creation of Allah activity

The words below are things that relate to Allah's (swt) creations. They need to be unscrambled.

1. sfhi ☐☐☐☐

2. nykoem ☐☐☐☐☐☐

3. rrevi ☐☐☐☐☐

4. wraobin   □□□□□□□
5. etre   □□□□
6. rdbi   □□□□
7. uldco   □□□□□
8. uresqilr □□□□□□□□
9. gofr   □□□□
10. tftyubre □□□□□□□□

Which of these creations do you
see in the sky?
on the ground?
in the water?

Answers (1) fish   (2) monkey   (3) river   (4) rainbow   (5) tree   (6) bird   (7) cloud   (8) squirrel   (9) frog   (10) butterfly